How To Draw
101 Funny
Animals

Licensed exclusively to Top That Publishing Ltd
Tide Mill Way, Woodbridge, Suffolk, IP12 1AP, UK
www.topthatpublishing.com
Copyright © 2014 Tide Mill Media

Lion

Pig

Lobster

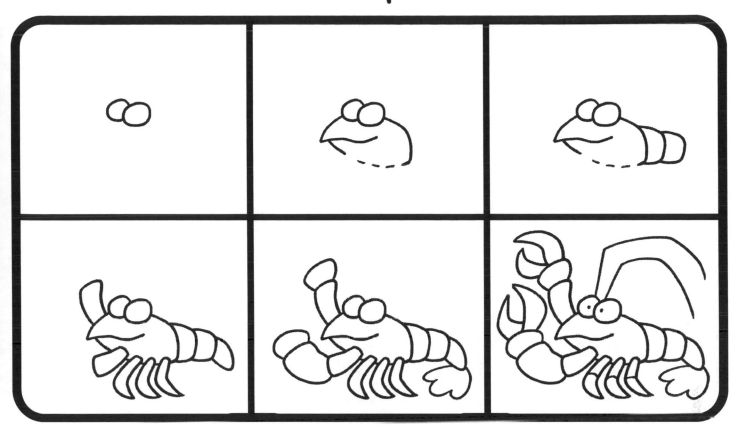

Kangaroo

Eagle

Chimpanzee

cat

Turtle

Dog

Baboon

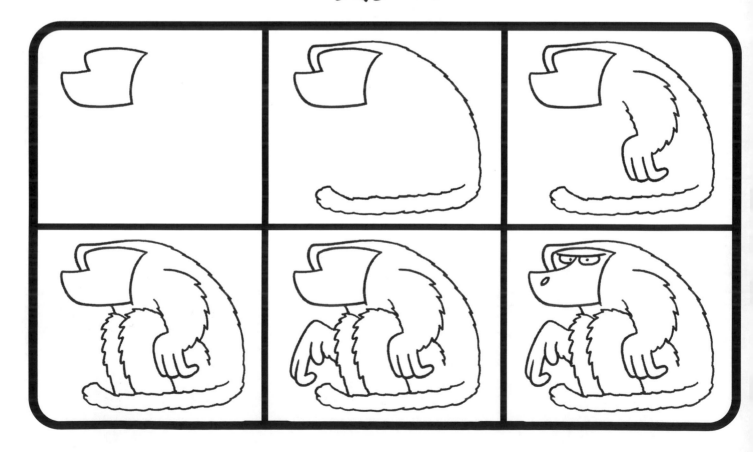

Fish

Tiger

Hedgehog

Kiwi

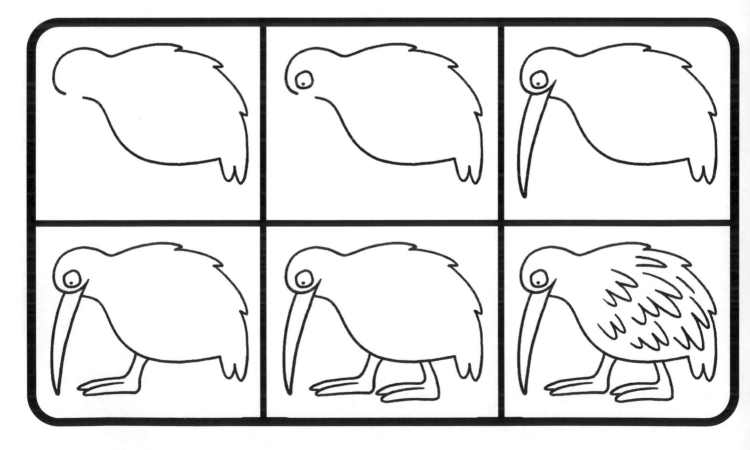

Parrot

Stag Beetle

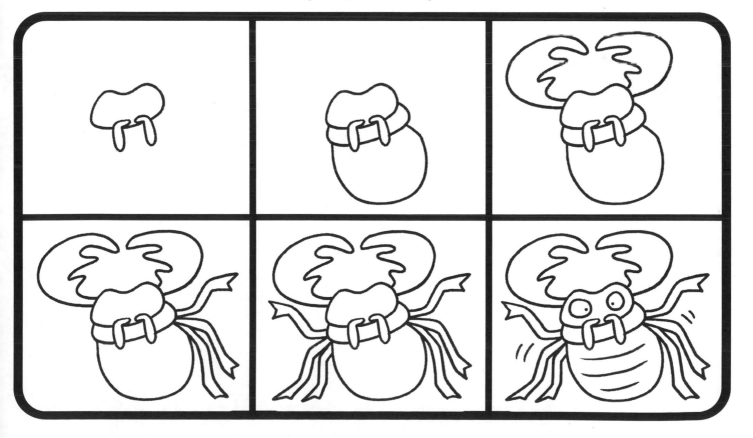

Anteater

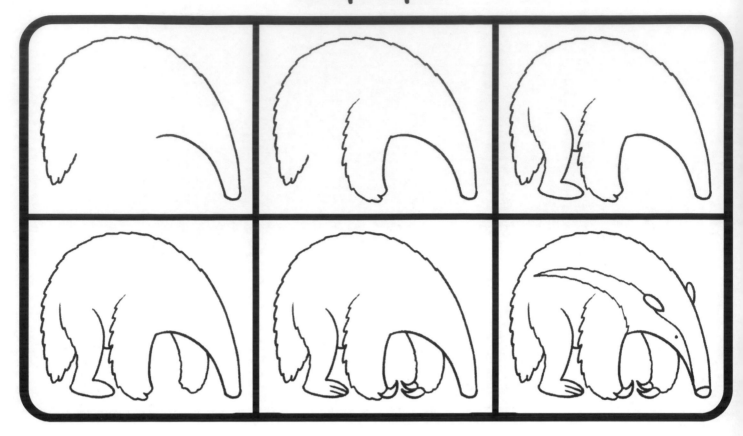

Chicken

Budgie

orang-utan

Rhino

Bat

Squirrel

Donkey

Toad

Owl

crab

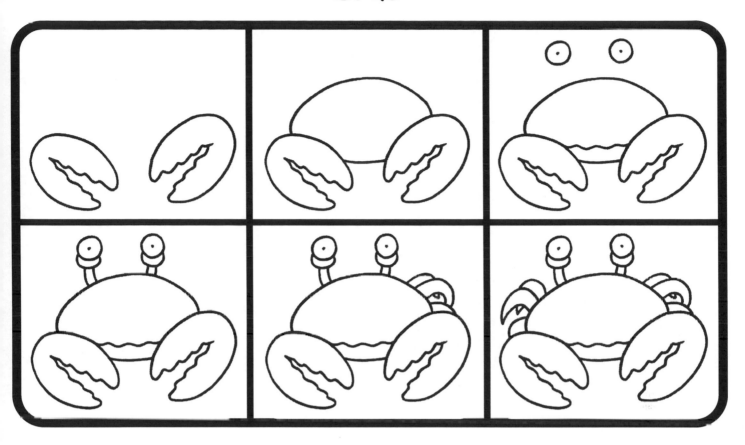

Dolphin

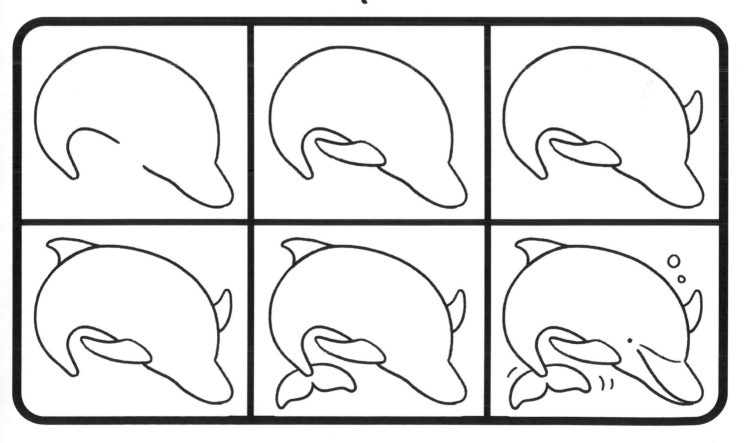

Cow

Rat

Seal

Tortoise

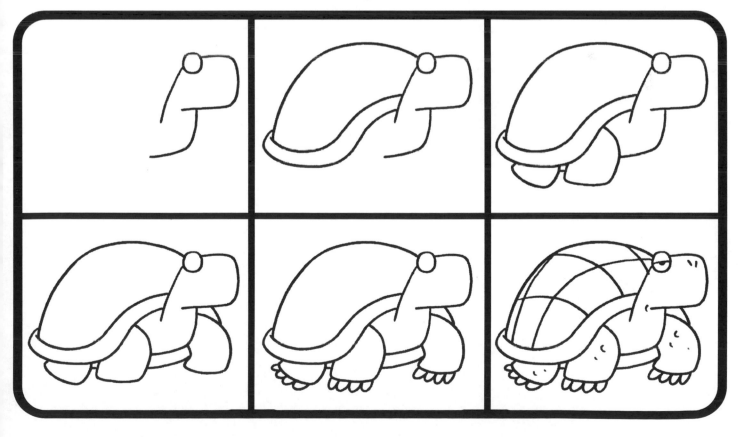

camel

Ant

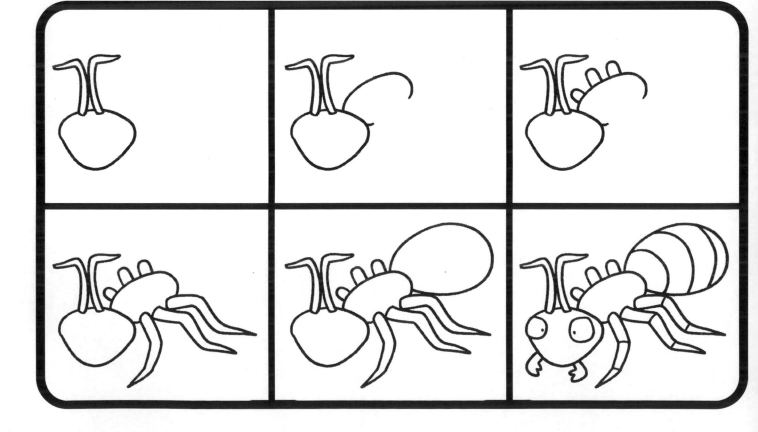

Peacock

Jellyfish

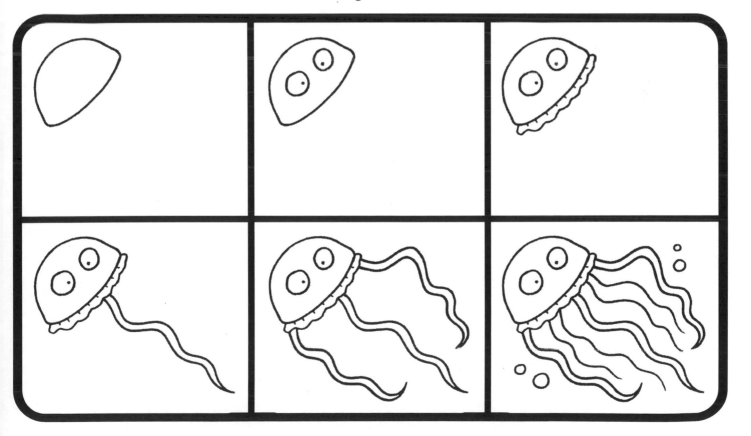

otter

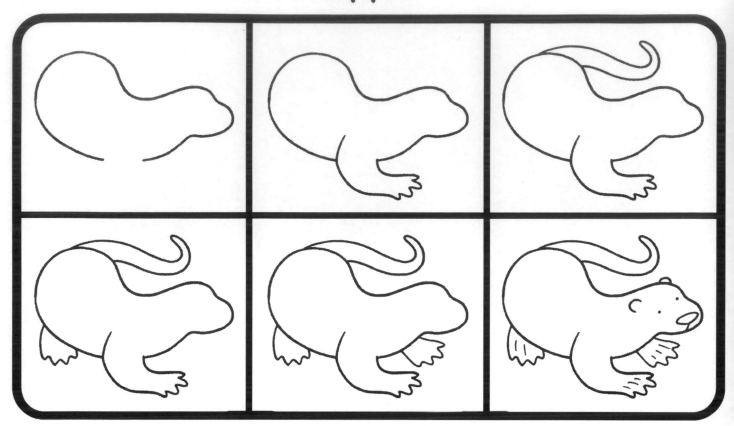

Zebra

Snail

Chameleon

Rabbit

Sheep

Panda

Snake

orca

Toucan

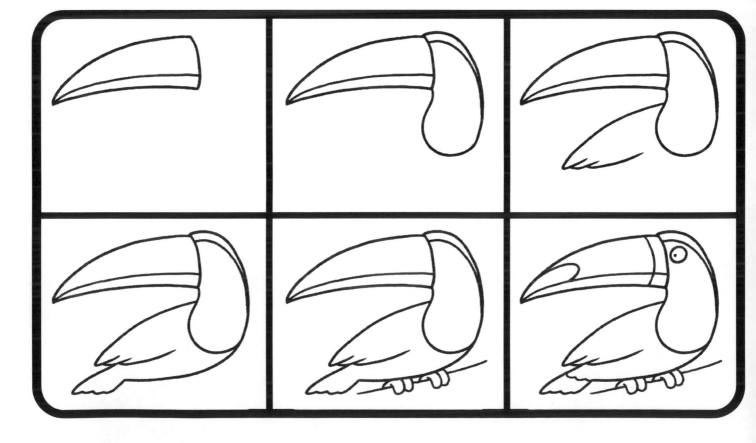

Lemur

Bison

Horse

Penguin

Elephant

Frog

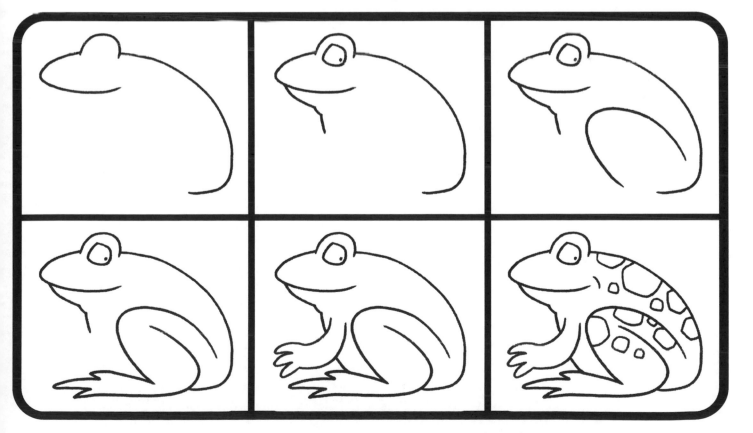

Shark

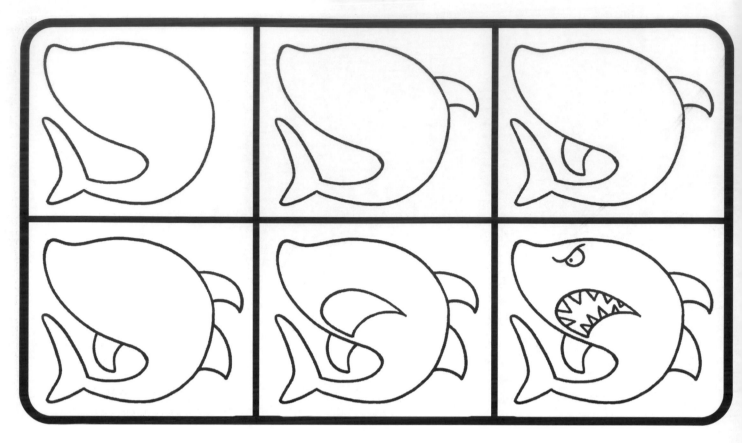

Goat

Panther

Kingfisher

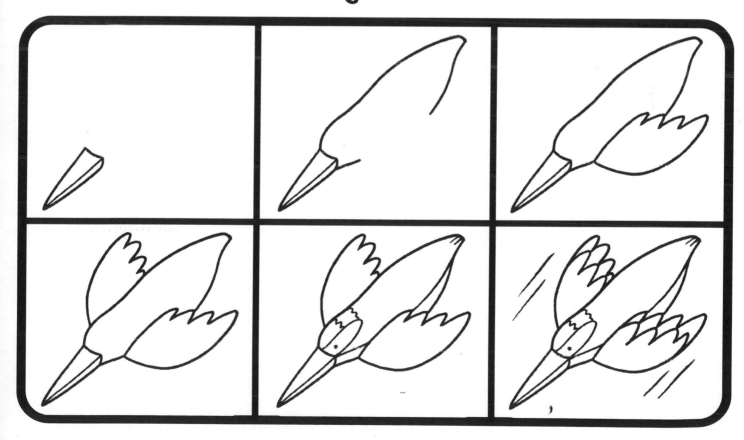

Grasshopper

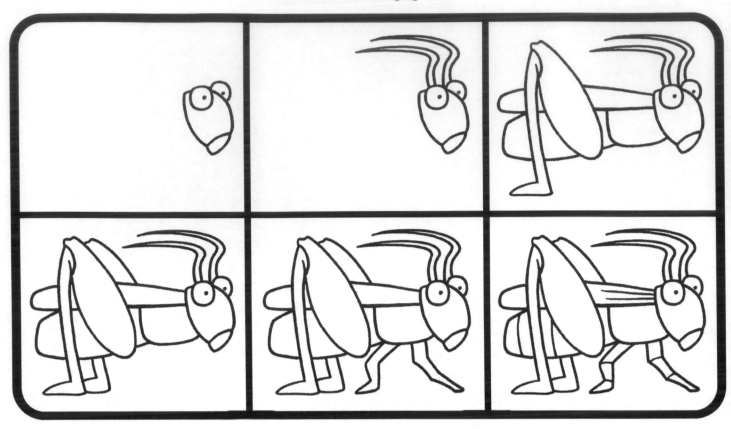

Squid

Duck

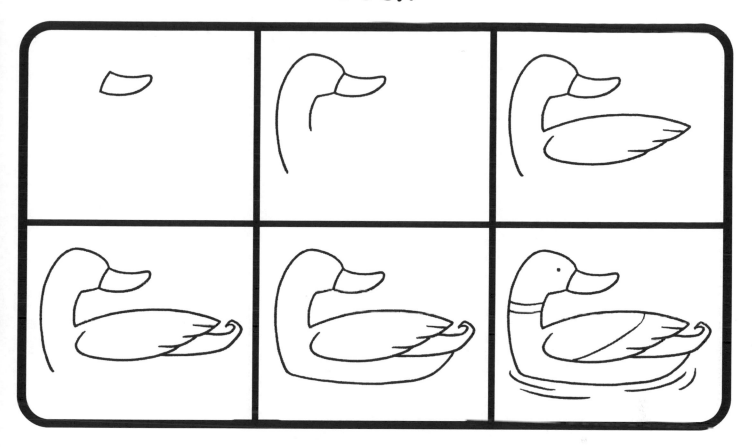

Porcupine

Humpback Whale

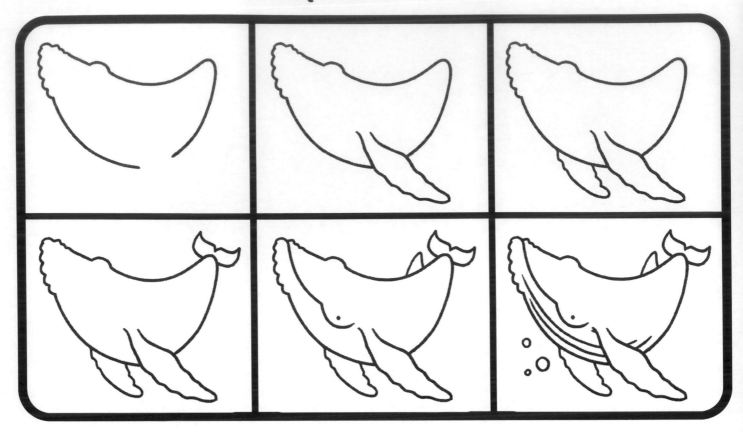

Beaver

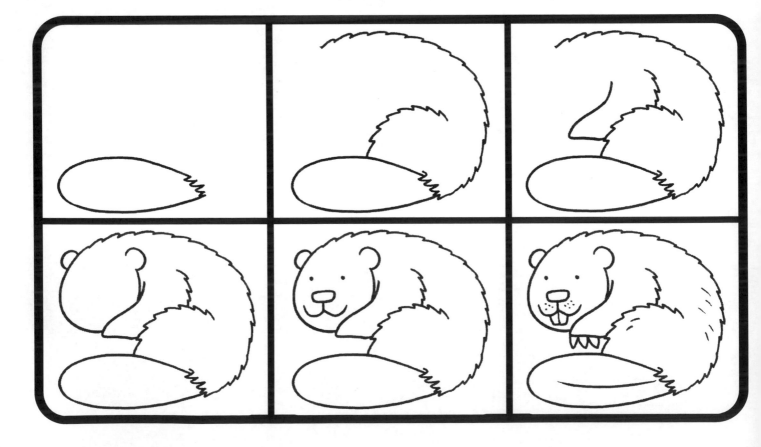

Koala

Walrus

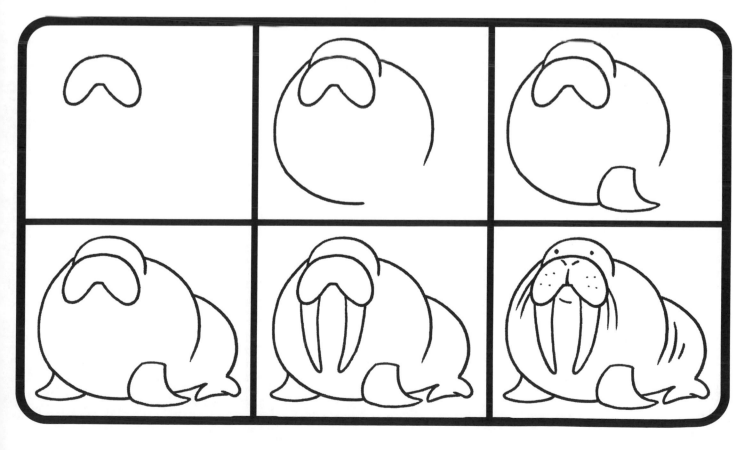

Spider

Mouse

Flamingo

Bear

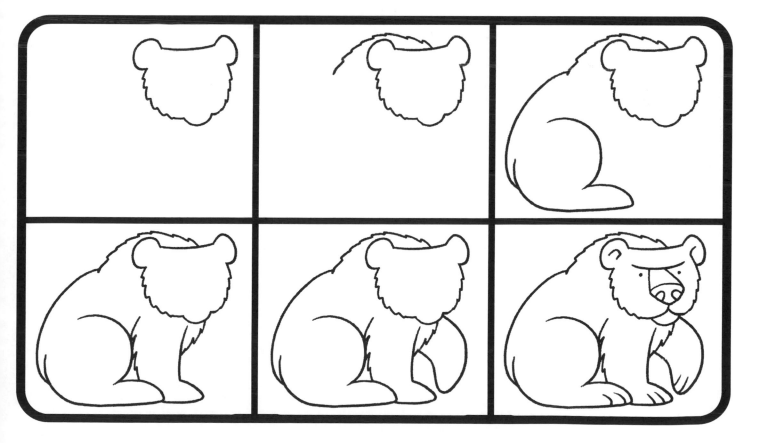

Sloth

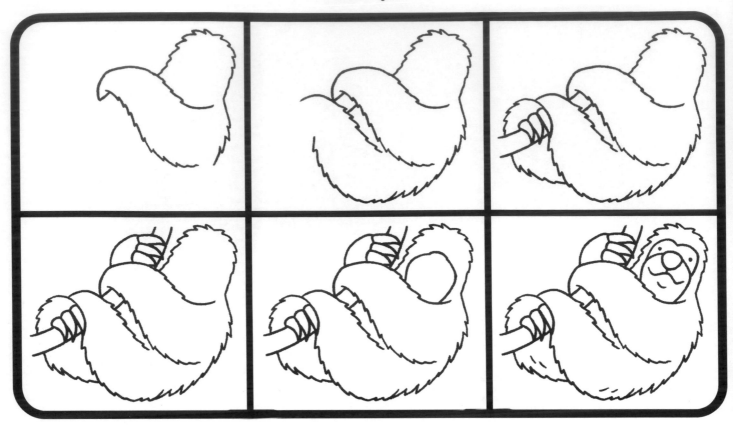

Hippo

Buffalo

Dragonfly

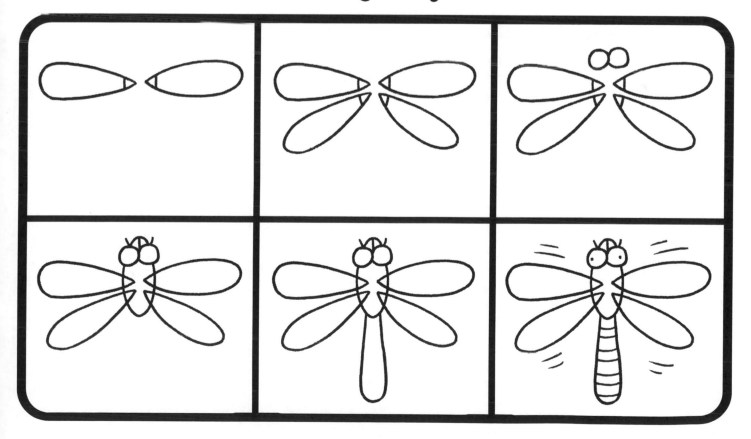

Cheetah

Shrimp

Monkey

Heron

Puffin

Armadillo

octopus

Bee

ostrich

Gorilla

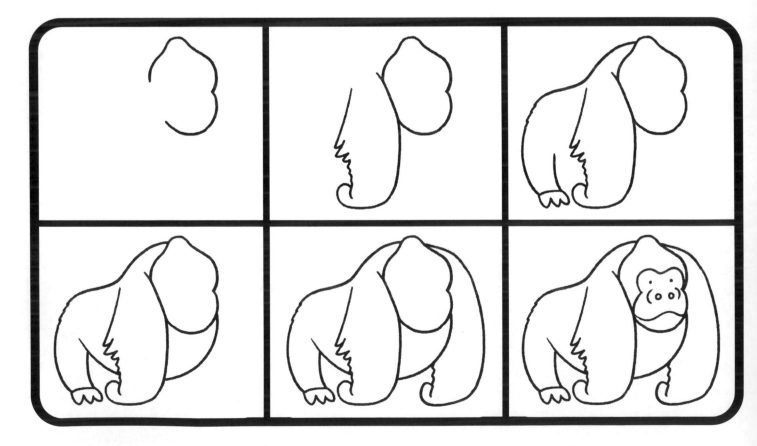

cuttlefish

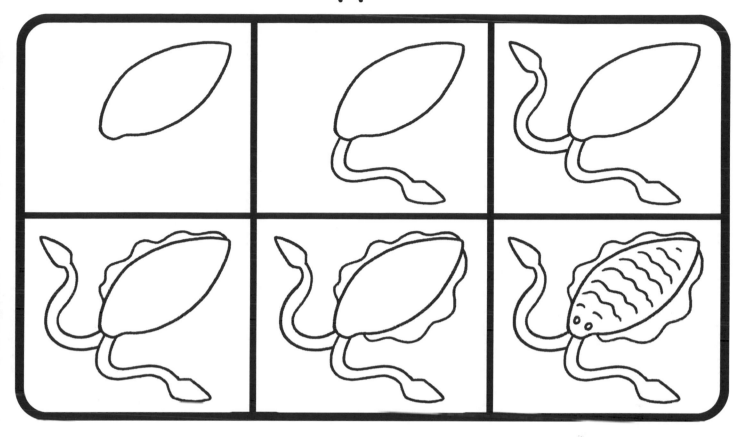

Ladybird

Swan

Manta Ray

Blue Whale

Crocodile

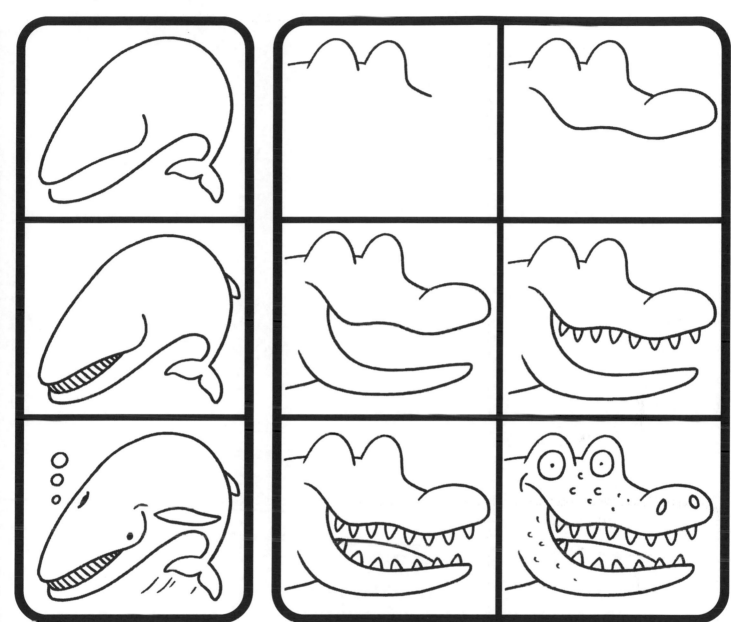

Worm

Wolf

Mole

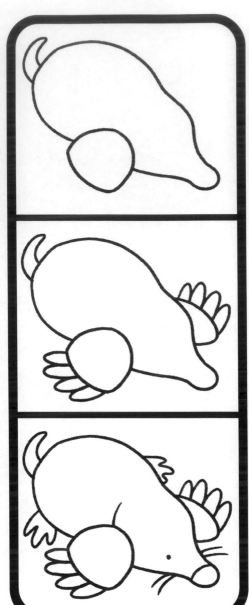

Angler Fish

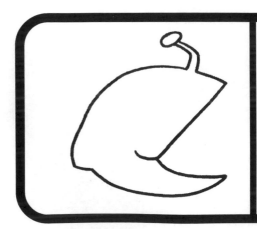

Starfish

Polar Bear

Hammerhead Shark

House fly

Woodpecker

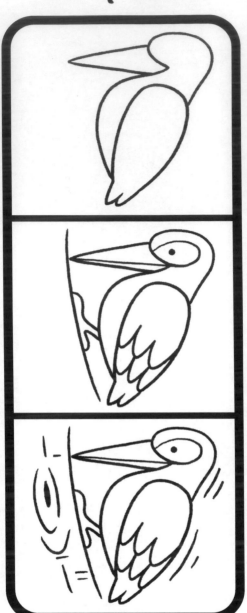

Sperm Whale

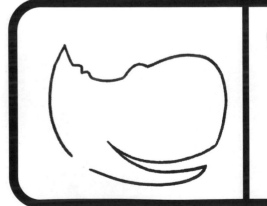  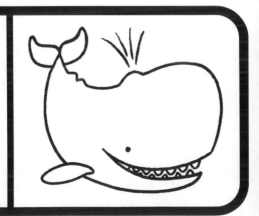

Angel Fish

Cobra

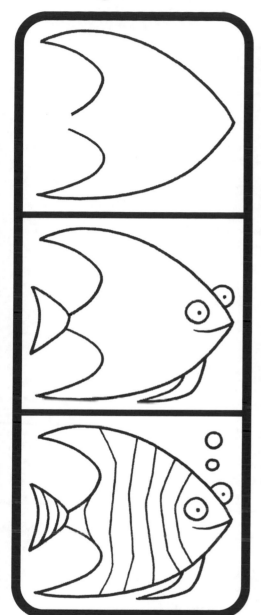

Butterfly

Other titles in the 'How to draw' series:

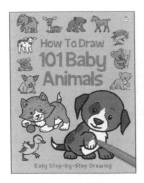

978-1-84956-987-3

978-1-84956-608-7

978-1-78244-484-8

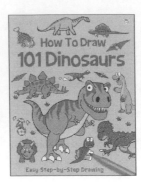

978-1-78244-021-5

978-1-78244-536-4

978-1-84956-605-6

978-1-84956-607-0

978-1-84956-988-0

978-1-78244-486-2

978-1-78244-485-5

978-1-84956-616-2

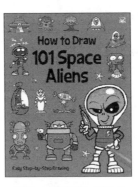

978-1-78244-483-1

978-1-84956-989-7

Practice Page

Practice Page

Printed in Great Britain
by Amazon